C000008231

SHORT CUTS
TO
PERCENTAGES

30 second CHALLENGE

by Norman D Lock
cover illustration by Peter Owen

Ladybird

Ladybird books are widely available, but in case of difficulty may be ordered by post
or telephone from: Ladybird Books – Cash Sales Department
Littlegate Road Paignton Devon TQ3 3BE Telephone 01803 554761

Published by Ladybird Books Ltd Loughborough Leicestershire UK
Ladybird Books Inc Auburn Maine 04210 USA

Test 1

1	7
2	x 3
3	add on nine
4	÷ 2
5	divide by three
6	n^2
7	double it
8	4 extra
9	÷ 9
10	multiply by three

What is your answer?

Check your answer at the back of the book.

Record your time on the Record Sheet.

Test 2

1	£5
2	times by 8
3	half of this
4	half of this
5	£8 more
6	share equally between two
7	x 5
8	+ £5
9	$\frac{1}{2}$ of this
10	$\frac{1}{2}$ of this

What is your answer?

Check your answer at the back of the book.

Record your time on the Record Sheet.

Test 3

1	six
2	n^2
3	÷ 4
4	times by 3
5	minus three
6	share into 6 equal parts
7	x 8
8	add on ten
9	divide by 7
10	multiply by 8

What is your answer?

Check your answer at the back of the book.

Record your time on the Record Sheet.

Test 4

1	£12
2	÷ 3
3	increase by £3
4	8 lots of this amount
5	share equally among 7 people
6	remove £3
7	x 7
8	double this amount
9	subtract £15
10	÷ 5

What is your answer?

Check your answer at the back of the book.

Record your time on the Record Sheet.

Test 5

Percentages are simply a type of fraction.

The symbol used for percentages is %. This stands for **'per cent'** which means **'out of a hundred'**.

So:

50% means $\frac{50}{100} = \frac{1}{2}$

25% means $\frac{25}{100} = \frac{1}{4}$

75% means $\frac{75}{100} = \frac{3}{4}$

$33\frac{1}{3}\%$ is equivalent to $\frac{1}{3}$

$66\frac{2}{3}\%$ is equivalent to $\frac{2}{3}$

- **Learn these off by heart so that you can use them very quickly.**

1	£8
2	4 lots of this
3	50% of this
4	find 25%
5	x 9
6	add on £4
7	25% of this
8	find 50%
9	x 6
10	50% of this

What is your answer?

Check your answer at the back of the book.

Record your time on the Record Sheet.

Test 6

1	36
2	$\sqrt{n}$
3	x 8
4	find 50%
5	50% of this
6	find 25%
7	times by nine
8	add on 13
9	75% of this
10	find $33\frac{1}{3}$%

What is your answer?

Check your answer at the back of the book.

Record your time on the Record Sheet.

Test 7

1	£20
2	75% of this
3	find $33\frac{1}{3}$%
4	multiply by 9
5	subtract £3
6	50% of this
7	find $66\frac{2}{3}$%
8	÷ 2
9	x 4
10	find 50%

What is your answer?

Check your answer at the back of the book.

Record your time on the Record Sheet.

Test 8

1	seven
2	n^2
3	eleven more
4	$66\frac{2}{3}\%$ of this
5	find 25%
6	x 8
7	plus one
8	$\sqrt{n}$
9	$33\frac{1}{3}\%$ of this
10	multiply by 8

What is your answer?

Check your answer at the back of the book.

Record your time on the Record Sheet.

Test 9

1	£24
2	$66\frac{2}{3}\%$ of this
3	find 75%
4	50% of this
5	x 6
6	double it
7	divide by 9
8	25% of this
9	multiply by 7
10	double it

What is your answer?

Check your answer at the back of the book.

Record your time on the Record Sheet.

10% means $\frac{10}{100} = \frac{1}{10}$

As you know, to find $\frac{1}{10}$ of something you divide by 10. There is a quick way of doing this. Look at these examples:

$$\begin{array}{ccc} H & T & U \\ & 4 & 0 \div 10 \\ = & & 4 \end{array}$$

$$\begin{array}{ccc} H & T & U \\ 3 & 5 & 0 \div 10 \\ = & 3 & 5 \end{array}$$

The numbers move **one** place to the right. We can do the same with money.

10% of £12 or $\frac{1}{10}$ of £12

£12.00 ÷ 10

= £1.20

10% of £3.70 or $\frac{1}{10}$ of £3.70

£3.70 ÷ 10

= £0.37 (or 37p)

10% of 90p or $\frac{1}{10}$ of 90p

£0.90 ÷ 10

= £0.09 (or 9p)

1	fifty
2	find 10%
3	× 4
4	seven extra
5	$33\frac{1}{3}\%$ of this
6	n^2
7	remove eleven
8	50% of this
9	− 15
10	10% of this

What is your answer?

Check your answer at the back of the book.

Record your time on the Record Sheet.

Test 11

1	£32
2	deduct £7
3	find 10%
4	double it
5	add £4
6	10% of this
7	5 lots of this
8	double it
9	double it
10	10% of this

What is your answer?

Check your answer at the back of the book.

Record your time on the Record Sheet.

Test 12

1	£100
2	find 75%
3	minus £3
4	find 50%
5	÷ 9
6	10% of this
7	x 5
8	25% of this
9	find 50%
10	÷ 5

What is your answer?

Check your answer at the back of the book.

Record your time on the Record Sheet.

Test 13

1	£150
2	find 10%
3	$33\frac{1}{3}\%$ of this
4	x 6
5	subtract £9
6	find $66\frac{2}{3}\%$
7	50% of this
8	find 10%
9	times by 4
10	10% of this

What is your answer?

Check your answer at the back of the book.

Record your time on the Record Sheet.

Test 14

1	900
2	50% of this
3	find 10%
4	$\div 9$
5	+ 3
6	n^2
7	75% of this
8	$\div 6$
9	add 22
10	10% of this

What is your answer?

Check your answer at the back of the book.

Record your time on the Record Sheet.

Now that you know how to find 10%, finding 20%, 30%, 40%, etc is easy.

For example, **30% is 3 lots of 10%.**

Look at this:

Find 30% and 70% of £9:

10% is $\frac{1}{10}$ of £9.00, so

10% is   £0.90

30% is   3 x £0.90 = £2.70
(3 lots of 9 ten penny coins, which is 27 ten penny coins = £2.70)

70% is $\frac{7}{10}$ of £9.00

70% is 7 x £0.90 = £6.30

For 20%, 40%, 60% and 80% you can also use another method.

$20\% = \frac{20}{100} = \frac{2}{10} = \frac{1}{5}$

$40\% = \frac{40}{100} = \frac{4}{10} = \frac{2}{5}$

$60\% = \frac{60}{100} = \frac{6}{10} = \frac{3}{5}$

$80\% = \frac{80}{100} = \frac{8}{10} = \frac{4}{5}$

For example, to find 60% of £15 you could use:

Method 1:

10% of £15.00 = £1.50
60% is 6 x £1.50 = £9.00

or **Method 2:**

60% is $\frac{3}{5}$

$\frac{1}{5}$ of £15.00 = £3.00

$\frac{3}{5}$ or 60% = 3 x £3.00

          = £9.00

1	forty
2	find 30%
3	double it
4	+ 1
5	$\sqrt{n}$
6	times by 7
7	double it
8	20% of this
9	find 50%
10	n^2

What is your answer?

Check your answer at the back of the book.

Record your time on the Record Sheet.

Test 16

1	£20
2	90% of this
3	add on £16
4	find 50%
5	deduct £10
6	40% of this
7	minus £2
8	find 25%
9	x 5
10	find 70%

What is your answer?

Check your answer at the back of the book.

Record your time on the Record Sheet.

Test 17

1	ten
2	n^2
3	+ 21
4	$\sqrt{n}$
5	times by 5
6	remove 5
7	find 80%
8	75% of this
9	find 50%
10	multiply by four

What is your answer?

Check your answer at the back of the book.

Record your time on the Record Sheet.

Test 18

1	£30
2	60% of this
3	find $33\frac{1}{3}\%$
4	x 9
5	plus £6
6	80% of this
7	find 75%
8	10% of this
9	deduct £3
10	times by 7

What is your answer?

Check your answer at the back of the book.

Record your time on the Record Sheet.

Test 19

1	five hundred
2	find 40%
3	50% of this
4	$\sqrt{n}$
5	70% of this
6	n^2
7	seven more
8	divide by 8
9	x 10
10	find 30%

What is your answer?

Check your answer at the back of the book.

Record your time on the Record Sheet.

Test 20

1	£50
2	find 60%
3	80% of this
4	find $66\frac{2}{3}$%
5	+ £12
6	divide equally into 4 parts
7	x 9
8	£3 less than this
9	find 90%
10	÷ 6

What is your answer?

Check your answer at the back of the book.

Record your time on the Record Sheet.

Test 21

1	£12
2	20% of this
3	add on 10p
4	double it
5	find 40%
6	30% of this
7	multiply by 7
8	80p extra
9	x 8
10	70% of this

What is your answer?

Check your answer at the back of the book.

Record your time on the Record Sheet.

1% means:
1 out of a hundred = $\frac{1}{100}$

To find $\frac{1}{100}$ of something you divide by 100. There is a quick way of doing this. When you divided by 10, you moved the numbers **one** place to the right.

When you divide by 100, move them **two** places to the right.

Look at these examples:

$$\begin{array}{ccc} H & T & U \\ 7 & 0 & 0 \div 100 \\ \rightarrow & \rightarrow & 7 \end{array}$$

$$\begin{array}{cccc} Th & H & T & U \\ 5 & 6 & 0 & 0 \div 100 \\ \rightarrow & \rightarrow & 5 & 6 \end{array}$$

Here are some money ones:

1% of £27 or $\frac{1}{100}$ of £27

$$£27.00 \div 100$$
$$= £\rightarrow\rightarrow.27$$
(or 27p)

1% of £6 or $\frac{1}{100}$ of £6

$$£6.00 \div 100$$
$$= £0.06$$
(or 6p)

1% of £134 or $\frac{1}{100}$ of £134

$$£134.00 \div 100$$
$$= £\rightarrow\rightarrow 1.34$$
(or £1.34)

1	six hundred
2	1% of this
3	x 9
4	subtract 14
5	find 10%
6	x 7
7	increase by 2
8	50% of this
9	find $66\frac{2}{3}\%$
10	n^2

What is your answer?

Check your answer at the back of the book.

Record your time on the Record Sheet.

Test 23

1	£25
2	find 1%
3	4 lots of this
4	x 13
5	add on £27
6	double it
7	60% of this
8	find 1%
9	÷ 4
10	50% of this

What is your answer?

Check your answer at the back of the book.

Record your time on the Record Sheet.

Test 24

1	£7
2	70% of this
3	plus 10p
4	x 10
5	find 1%
6	times by 8
7	multiply by 9
8	double it
9	£28 extra
10	1%

What is your answer?

Check your answer at the back of the book.

Record your time on the Record Sheet.

Test 25

1	50
2	x 6
3	1% of this
4	multiply by 9
5	double it
6	add 16
7	find 40%
8	divide by 7
9	times by 9
10	$33\frac{1}{3}$% of this

What is your answer?

Check your answer at the back of the book.

Record your time on the Record Sheet.

Test 26

1	£60
2	find 75%
3	double it
4	1% of this
5	x 7
6	add 70p
7	times by 8
8	find 1%
9	÷ 7
10	multiply by 9

What is your answer?

Check your answer at the back of the book.

Record your time on the Record Sheet.

If you can find 1% ($\frac{1}{100}$),
then it is easy to find
2%, 3%, 4%, etc.

For example,
3% is 3 lots of 1%.

Find 3% of £7:

1% is $\frac{1}{100}$ of £7.00

1%   = £0.07
           (or 7p)

3% is 3 x 7p = £0.21
           (or 21p)

Another example:

Find 7% of £12:

1% of £12.00 = £0.12
           (or 12p)

7% is 7 x 12p = £0.84
           (or 84p)

To find 5% you can either
use the method shown
above or find 10% (which
is easy to do) and then
halve it.

Look at these:

Find 5% of £9:

10% of £9.00 = £0.90
           (or 90p)

5% is half of 90p = £0.45
           (or 45p)

Find 5% of £24:

10% of £24.00 = £2.40

5% is half of £2.40
           = £1.20

1	£5
2	find 3%
3	x 4
4	double it
5	double it
6	double it
7	add 20p
8	times by 8
9	5% of this
10	75% of this

What is your answer?

Check your answer at the
back of the book.

Record your time on the
Record Sheet.

Test 28

1	200
2	find 8%
3	÷ 2
4	n^2
5	plus 6
6	50% of this
7	take off 10
8	$\sqrt{n}$
9	x 100
10	11% of this

What is your answer?

Check your answer at the back of the book.

Record your time on the Record Sheet.

Test 29

1	£27
2	$33\frac{2}{3}$% of this
3	find 4%
4	6p more
5	share out into 6 equal parts
6	100 times this
7	x 9
8	an additional £7
9	5% of this
10	50% of this

What is your answer?

Check your answer at the back of the book.

Record your time on the Record Sheet.

Test 30

1	£9
2	find 6%
3	take away 5p
4	share out into 7 equal parts
5	x 9
6	double it
7	remove 1p
8	double it
9	20% of this
10	multiply by 7

What is your answer?

Check your answer at the back of the book.

Record your time on the Record Sheet.

Test 31

1	one thousand
2	8% of this
3	minus 16
4	$\sqrt{n}$
5	x 90
6	add on 80
7	find 7%
8	50% of this
9	75% of this
10	$66\frac{2}{3}\%$ of this

What is your answer?

Check your answer at the back of the book.

Record your time on the Record Sheet.

In this book you have learned a quick way to **divide** by 10 and 100.

To divide by 10 you move the numbers **one** place to the **right** to make the number smaller.

$$£15 \quad ÷ 10 \text{ or}$$
$$£15.00 ÷ 10$$
$$= £{→}1.50$$

To divide by 100 you move the numbers **two** places to the **right**.

$$£35 \quad ÷ 100 \text{ or}$$
$$£35.00 ÷ 100$$
$$= £{→→}.35$$
$$\text{(or 35p)}$$

To **multiply** by 10 you move the numbers **one** place to the **left**.

$$36p \text{ x } 10$$
$$£0.36 \text{ x } 10$$
$$= £3.60$$
$$£1.95 \text{ x } 10$$
$$= £19.50$$

To multiply by 100 you move the numbers **two** places to the **left**.

$$5p \text{ x } 100$$
$$£0.05 \text{ x } 100$$
$$= £5.00$$

$$£ 2.75 \text{ x } 100$$
$$= £275.00$$

1	7p
2	x 100
3	50% of this
4	x 10
5	÷ 7
6	find 10%
7	multiply by 6
8	1% of this
9	times by 9
10	double it

What is your answer?

Check your answer at the back of the book.

Record your time on the Record Sheet.

Test 33

1	£2.70
2	x 10
3	divide by 9
4	multiply by 8
5	25% of this
6	find 5%
7	x 7
8	times by 10
9	£9 added on
10	6% of this

What is your answer?

Check your answer at the back of the book.

Record your time on the Record Sheet.

Test 34

1	15p
2	x 100
3	double it
4	£6 extra
5	share out into 9 equal parts
6	multiply by 100
7	75% of this
8	find 50%
9	$66\frac{2}{3}\%$ of this
10	find 3%

What is your answer?

Check your answer at the back of the book.

Record your time on the Record Sheet.

Test 35

1	28p
2	times by 10
3	25% of this
4	9 lots of this
5	find 10%
6	divide by 7
7	x 100
8	6 times this
9	add on £6
10	find 2%

What is your answer?

Check your answer at the back of the book.

Record your time on the Record Sheet.

Test 36

1	£50
2	find 70%
3	double it
4	1% of this
5	x 8
6	remove 60p
7	find 50%
8	30% of this
9	double it
10	double it

What is your answer?

Check your answer at the back of the book.

Record your time on the Record Sheet.

You often see percentages written on signs in shop windows, especially during the sales, to tell you that certain items are reduced in price.

For example, you might have seen '10% off all computer games' or '25% off the price of a television'.

This is easy to work out.

Look at these examples:

A computer game normally costs £50. In the sale it is reduced in price by 10%. What does it now cost?

  10% of £50 =   £5
  £50 less £5 = £45
    It now costs £45.

A television normally costs £240. In a sale it is reduced in price by 25%. What does it now cost?

  25% of £240 =   £60
  £240 less £60 = £180
    It now costs   £180.

1	£10
2	take away 10%
3	x 5
4	add on £9
5	divide by 6
6	$33\frac{1}{3}\%$ of this
7	find 1%
8	times by 50
9	double it
10	x 20

What is your answer?

Check your answer at the back of the book.

Record your time on the Record Sheet.

Test 38

1	£20
2	less 25%
3	1% of this
4	x 4
5	double it
6	find 10%
7	multiply by four
8	x 100
9	add £2
10	7% of this

What is your answer?

Check your answer at the back of the book.

Record your time on the Record Sheet.

Test 39

1	£36
2	$33\frac{1}{3}$% off
3	÷ 6
4	9% of this
5	double it
6	times by 10
7	minus 20p
8	x 8
9	find 1%
10	divide by 7

What is your answer?

Check your answer at the back of the book.

Record your time on the Record Sheet.

Test 40

1	£80
2	find 75%
3	less 10%
4	÷ 6
5	multiply by 5
6	10% of this
7	minus £2
8	3 times this
9	find 10%
10	double it

What is your answer?

Check your answer at the back of the book.

Record your time on the Record Sheet.

Test 41

1	3p
2	x 100
3	multiply by 6
4	$66\frac{2}{3}\%$ of this
5	find 10%
6	50% of this
7	times by 7
8	add on 80p
9	take away 10%
10	divide by 9

What is your answer?

Check your answer at the back of the book.

Record your time on the Record Sheet.

Unfortunately you sometimes have to pay extra! Instead of having 10% off the price, sometimes you have to **add on** a certain percentage.

Here are two examples:
A meal costs £25 plus a 10% service charge. What is the full cost of the meal?

```
        £25.00
+ 10% £  2.50
        £27.50
```

The total bill is £27.50.

Some furniture costs £400 and there is a 2% delivery charge. What is the full cost?

1% of £400 = £4

```
       £400.00
+ 2% £    8.00
       £408.00
```

The total cost is £408.

1	£40
2	plus 10%
3	25% of this
4	take away £2
5	x 7
6	minus £3
7	10% off
8	÷ 6
9	find $33\frac{1}{3}\%$
10	multiply by 7

What is your answer?

Check your answer at the back of the book.

Record your time on the Record Sheet.

Test 43

1	£64
2	shared equally among 8 people
3	75% of this
4	x 10
5	double it
6	double it
7	deduct £30
8	find $66\frac{2}{3}$%
9	50% of this
10	add on 5%

What is your answer?

Check your answer at the back of the book.

Record your time on the Record Sheet.

Test 44

1	£500
2	plus 4%
3	+ £20
4	10% of this
5	divide by 9
6	find 1%
7	times by 8
8	double it
9	4p extra
10	plus 9%

What is your answer?

Check your answer at the back of the book.

Record your time on the Record Sheet.

Test 45

1	23p
2	x 100
3	take away £9
4	2% of this
5	double it
6	times by 10
7	divide by 7
8	times by 100
9	plus 10%
10	75% of this

What is your answer?

Check your answer at the back of the book.

Record your time on the Record Sheet.

Test 46

1	£5000
2	3% of this
3	find 50%
4	take away £3
5	÷ 8
6	x 6
7	1% of this
8	add on 6p
9	times by 100
10	plus 30%

What is your answer?

Check your answer at the back of the book.

Record your time on the Record Sheet.

Record Sheet

Date	Test No.	Time	Score
15th July	8	30 seconds	24

Record Sheet

Date	Test No.	Time	Score

Record Sheet

Date	Test No.	Time	Score

Record Sheet

Date	Test No.	Time	Score
25/04/99	21		